Simon's Cat

Simon's Cat

beyond the fence

by Simon Tofield

PENGUIN
CANADA

PENGUIN CANADA

Published by the Penguin Group

Penguin Group (Canada), 90 Eglinton Avenue East, Suite 700, Toronto, Ontario, Canada
M4P 2Y3 (a division of Pearson Canada Inc.)

Penguin Group (USA) Inc., 375 Hudson Street, New York, New York 10014, U.S.A.
Penguin Books Ltd, 80 Strand, London WC2R 0RL, England
Penguin Ireland, 25 St Stephen's Green, Dublin 2, Ireland (a division of Penguin Books Ltd)
Penguin Group (Australia), 250 Camberwell Road, Camberwell, Victoria 3124, Australia (a division of Pearson Australia Group Pty Ltd)
Penguin Books India Pvt Ltd, 11 Community Centre, Panchsheel Park, New Delhi — 110 017, India
Penguin Group (NZ), 67 Apollo Drive, Rosedale, North Shore 0745, Auckland, New Zealand (a division of Pearson New Zealand Ltd)
Penguin Books (South Africa) (Pty) Ltd, 24 Sturdee Avenue, Rosebank, Johannesburg 2196, South Africa

Penguin Books Ltd, Registered Offices: 80 Strand, London WC2R 0RL, England

Published in Canada by Penguin Group (Canada), a division of Pearson Canada, Inc., 2010. Published simultaneously in Great Britain by Canongate Books Ltd.,
14 High Street, Edinburgh EH1 1TE.

1 2 3 4 5 6 7 8 9 10

Copyright © Simon Tofield, 2010

Manufactured in Canada.

LIBRARY AND ARCHIVES CANADA CATALOGUING IN PUBLICATION

Tofield, Simon
    Simon's cat : beyond the fence / Simon Tofield.

ISBN 978-0-14-317340-3

    1. Cats—Caricatures and cartoons. 2. Cats—Humor.
3. English wit and humor, Pictorial. I. Title.

NC1479.T645S42 2010   741.5'941   C2010-903092-3

British Library Cataloguing in Publication data available

Visit the Penguin Group (Canada) website at www.penguin.ca

Special and corporate bulk purchase rates available; please see
www.penguin.ca/corporatesales or call 1-800-810-3104, ext. 2477 or 2474

In memory of my good friend Owain Jones

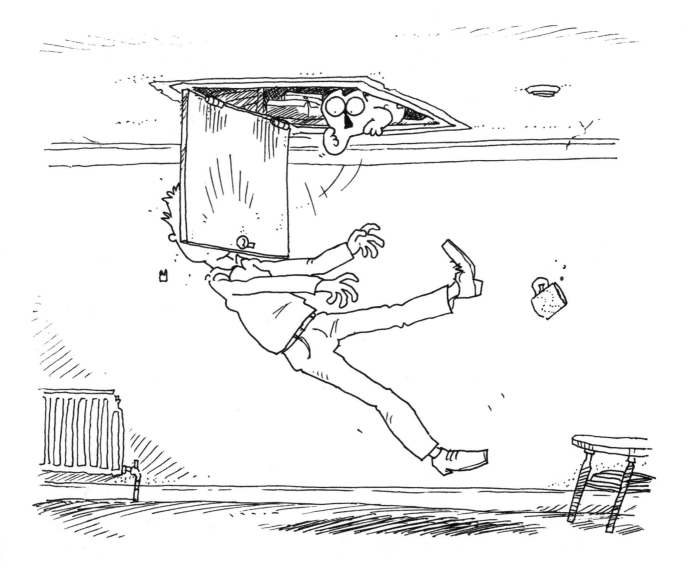

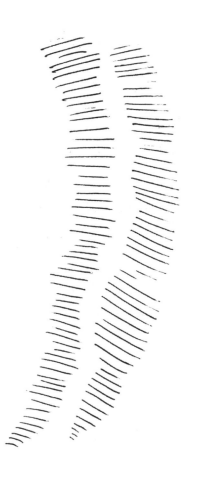

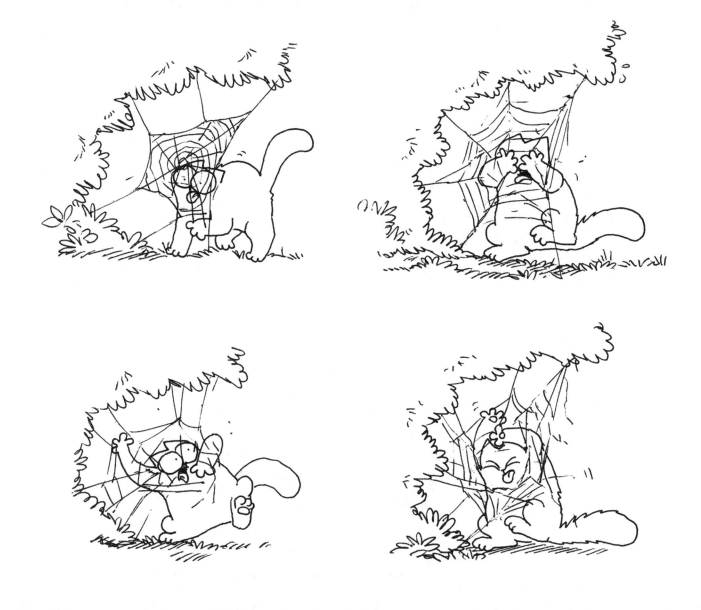

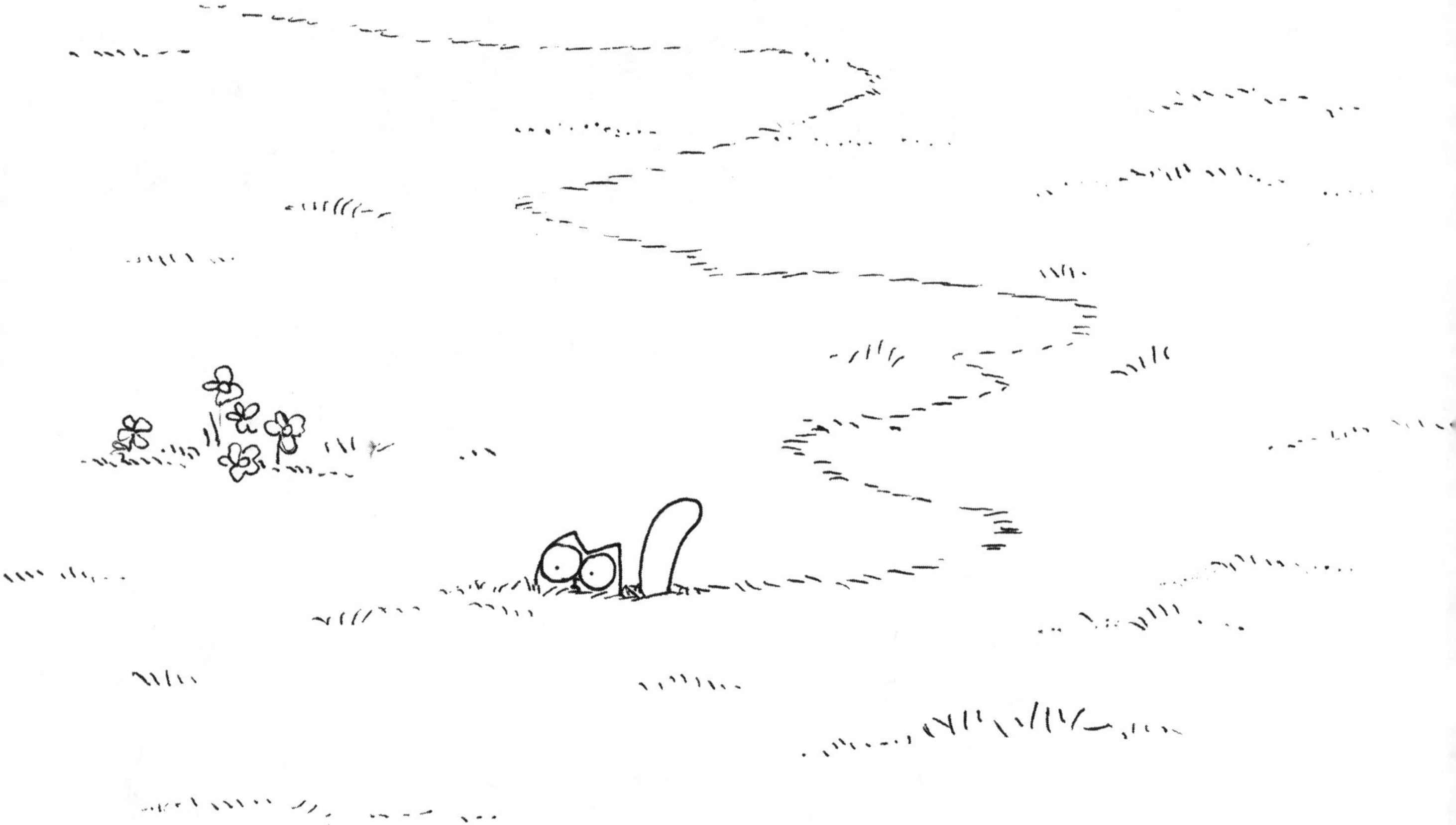

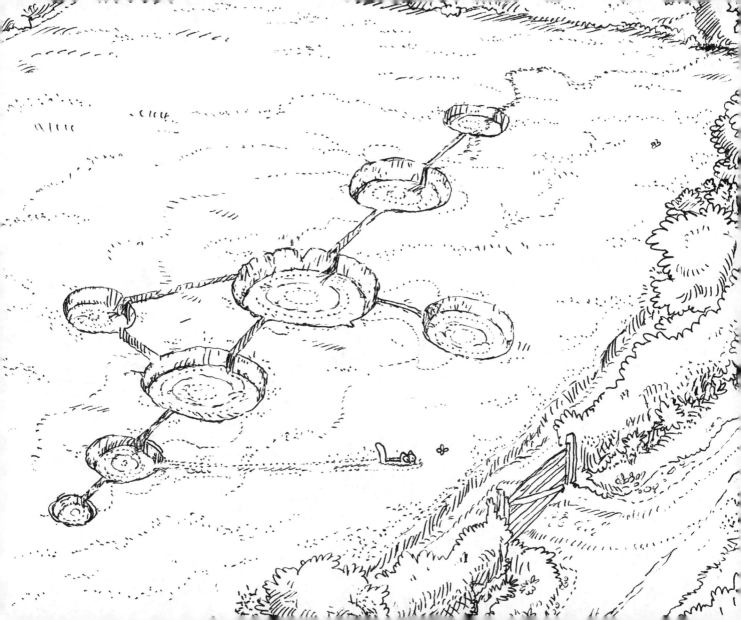

Acknowledgements

Thanks to Kirk Redmond, Don Evans, Martha and Tom Holdom, Barry Geal, Alan Proctor, Mike Staxman Cook, Matthew and Amelia Shaw, Sean and Kirsty, Alydia Tobin-White, Sarah and Nick Alexander, Chris Gavin, Sarah and Tim Fancourt, Walt and Margaret Randall, Nigel Pay, Mike Bell, Daniel Greaves, Mark Burton, Nick Davies and the Canongate team, Robert Kirby and Duncan Hayes at UA and my four cats for providing endless inspiration.

Simon Tofield's first book, *Simon's Cat,* was a
Sunday Times bestseller in the UK and has been
published in over twenty countries around the
world. This new book combines Simon's love for
cats and the British countryside.

For all your Simon's Cat goodies,
check out the webshop at

www.simonscat.com